TIME FOR an adventure

Hi there! My name is Joaquin (pronounced Wah-Keen) The Dog. My mom and dad named me Joaquin because they thought it was funny and sounds like "walking the dog". We all love to go for walks, and I love new adventures.

Joaquin The Dog

New York City is one of the most famous cities in the entire world! It is called the City That Never Sleeps, and even though I sleep a lot, I still wanted to visit!

BOARDING PASS

FLIGHT   **TO** NYC   **FROM** SAN

PASSENGER   Joaquin The Dog

DATE   TIME   BOARDING

GATE   SEAT

E-TICKET

PASSENGER
Joaquin The Dog

FLIGHT   TIME

GATE   SEAT

E-TICKET

In New York, people walk everywhere. But my little legs got tired from all that walking, so I took yellow taxis and the subway. The subway is an underground train that runs under the city super fast!

When I was ready to run around, we headed to Central Park. It is right in the middle of New York and provides green space in a concrete jungle. There are lots of gardens, fountains and events in the park! I went during the winter, and there was an ice skating rink.

I've never seen so many tall buildings in one place! One of the most recognized buildings in New York, the Empire State Building, is over 1,400 feet tall. Sometimes it is lit up to support sports teams, or celebrate holidays. The tip of the Empire State Building is struck by lightning an average of 25 times per year!

Besides my Mama, I met the next coolest lady in the US. The Statue of Liberty is so famous! It was a present from France as a sign of friendship. She is called Lady Liberty and represents freedom. You can take a ferry to Liberty Island to see her up close, or even climb to the top!

Right next to Liberty Island is Ellis Island. It is where people moving to the United States from other places arrived by boat in the 18 and 1900s! More than 12 million people entered the US through Ellis Island, even my Mama's great grandparents. You can visit the museum and search for your relatives if they entered the US through Ellis Island, too!

I thought the Empire State Building was tall until I saw One World Trade Center! It is the tallest building in the US at 1,776 feet tall. The 1776' height is special, because USA got its independence in 1776. The building is named the Freedom Tower!

I visited the memorial to September 11th and paid respects to all who lost their lives during the attack on the Twin Tower buildings in 2001. There is a serene park to remember and reflect.

The main street of New York's financial district is Wall Street. It is where you find the New York Stock Exchange. Wall Street got its name from the 1600s, when there was a wall built to defend the city from intruders! There is no wall there anymore, but the name is still Wall Street.

Chinatown is a busy neighborhood full of restaurants, shops and activity. You can find the neighborhood locals in Columbus Park doing the martial art Tai Chi, or playing chess and mahjong, a Chinese game with tiles.

Times Square named itself after the New York Times newspaper, and it's the center of it all! You can feel all the energy. It made me want to do zoomies - a full circle view of lights, lots of entertainment, and PEOPLE!

I ♥ NY

The glitz, the glam, the fame - Broadway and Times Square have it all! Broadway is the big time for theater and stage performing actors. The most popular Broadway show of all time in New York is the Lion King. It is the true king of Broadway.

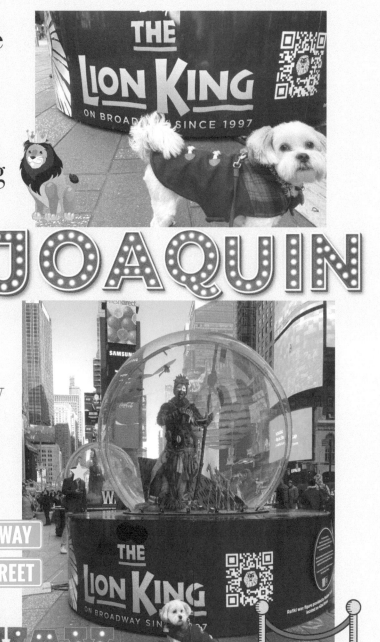

JOAQUIN

BROADWAY

TICKET

BROADWAY

2ND STREET

Like a true New Yorker, I did a lot of walking. North of Central Park is where you will find Harlem. Once a Dutch neighborhood called Haarlem, then home to many Jewish and Italian immigrants, Harlem is now a cultural center for African Americans, with cool jazz clubs, soul food, and lots of activity.

Located in Harlem is the famous Apollo Theater, a music club that was so important for many types of American music like jazz, blues, soul, swing. It launched the careers of many famous musicians.

Joaquin
The Dog

If you go all the way to the other side of Manhattan, you can visit a different part of New York City. The Brooklyn Bridge connects Manhattan and Brooklyn and these little legs walked across the whole thing! It was the longest suspension bridge at the time it was built, and I believe it, because I was tired!

Brooklyn

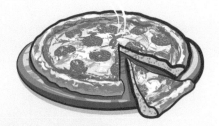

DUMBO is not a friendly elephant like I thought; it's a neighborhood in Brooklyn. Dumbo stands for "Down Under the Manhattan Bridge Overpass". Look at the beautiful views of Manhattan!

Grand Central Terminal is so beautiful. It's where lots of trains travel to and from New York. It has high ceilings and looks so nice. It is also a little magical. If one person stands in one corner of the tiled wall and another stands on the opposite side, they can whisper to each other, and hear each other across the room!

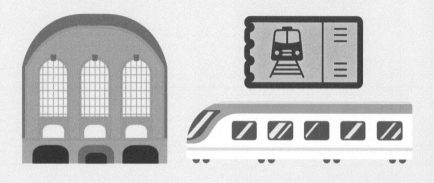

Interested in shopping until you drop? Fifth Avenue is the place for you! But be sure to bring your allowance, it's one of the most expensive shopping streets in the world, and is nicknamed Millionaire's Row.

If you want a great view of the city, you can go to the top of Rockefeller Center. I was so lucky to visit New York in December to see the ice skating rink and the biggest Christmas tree I've ever seen. They're both in Rockefeller Center!

One of the buildings in Rockefeller Center is Radio City Music Hall or "The Showplace of the Nation". This is where the Rockettes, a dance performing group, do their shows. There are also concerts, and now Radio City Music Hall is a National Landmark.

Greenwich Village is a neighborhood that was full of artists and was nicknamed "the bohemian capital". Lots of activism and social justice movements began here! Greenwich Village has Washington Square Park, too, a great place to meet some new pups!

Hudson Yards is a new neighborhood and has one of the weirdest buildings I've ever seen. It's called the Vessel, and looks like a spaceship! Dogs can go in!

New York has some of the most famous museums in the whole world! The Metropolitan Museum of Art (or The Met), the MoMa, the Guggenheim, and the Museum of Tolerance. Each year The Met has some kind of fancy ball for celeb-paw-ties. I love to play ball, and hope to go one day!

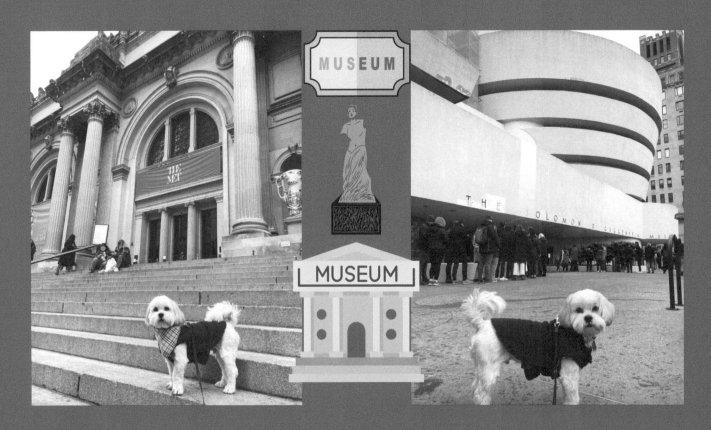

They also have fun museums that are more interactive like the Intrepid Sea, Air and Space Museum, the Museum of Natural History, a spy museum, and even an Ice Cream Museum.

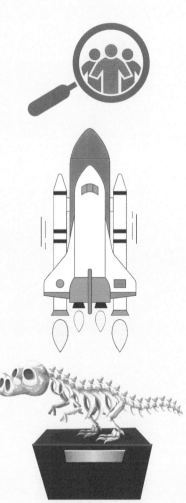

The High Line is another park, but it is overtop the street! It goes along an old railway line. You can see some great views of the city from the High Line.

There are so many more fun things to do in New York - visit the animals at the Bronx Zoo, ride the roller coaster at Coney Island, see a concert at Carnegie Hall or Lincoln Center, visit the famous Plaza Hotel, take a boat trip, see a concert or game at Madison Square Garden, go to one of the many food markets, or go to a baseball game. I can't wait to come back and do it all!

DID YOU KNOW?

 Spaghetti and meatballs, pasta primavera, eggs benedict and ice cream cones were all invented in New York City

 More Chinese people live in New York City than any other city outside of Asia. More Jewish people live in NYC than any other city outside of Israel.

 New Yorkers Speak More Than 800 Languages, many households speak more than one language and one-third are born overseas.

 Originally New Amsterdam was named by the Dutch, but in 1664, the English took over and renamed the city in the Duke of York's honor.

DID YOU KNOW?

 NYC has many nicknames - The Big Apple, Empire City, City of Dreams, & The City That Never Sleeps.

 The first pizzeria in the US, Lombardi's, opened in New York City in 1905 and is still open today!

 New York has the biggest population of any US city, 1 in 38 people in the United States are New Yorkers.

 New York City became the first capital of the United States in 1789.

 New York City's Federal Reserve Bank has the largest gold storage in the world. The vault is 80 feet below street level and contains $90 billion in gold.

The Lenape People

The Lenape, Manhattan's original inhabitants, called the island Manahatta, which means "hilly island", rich in fruits, nuts, birds, and animals. There were lots of fish and shellfish, seals, whales, dolphins and birds. In the 1600s, the Dutch arrived and met the Lenape. At first, they were friendly to each other, and shared land and traded guns, beads and wool for furs. There is an old tale that the Dutch "purchased" Manahattan island from the Lenape in 1626, and then forced the Lenape people to leave the island. The Lenape inhabited current day New York City to Philadelphia, New Jersey, much of eastern Pennsylvania and part of Delaware. Today there is a Lenape center in New York full of information about Lenape history and culture and taking care of the lands.

https://storymaps.arcgis.com/stories/56b1d134920d46c6ac2462c1344eeb3f

Oscar and the Magic Table

Keith Harvey

Illustrated by Lauren Beard

Award Publications Limited

ISBN 978-1-84135-922-9

Written by Keith Harvey
Illustrated by Lauren Beard

First published by Tiberius Publishing Limited

This edition first published by Award Publications Limited 2013

Published by Award Publications Limited,
The Old Riding School, The Welbeck Estate,
Worksop, Nottinghamshire, S80 3LR

www.awardpublications.co.uk

13 1

Printed in China

For Oscar

Oscar was feeling
very unhappy.

Great Aunty Jill was coming to stay.
He always liked her staying because she was so much fun.

But his mother had just told him that he couldn't stay up for dinner with them.

The problem was Oscar's terrible table manners. He was forever getting into trouble. He would put his elbows on the table, eat off his knife, and leave the table before everyone had finished.

At dinner-time the day before, when Oscar's father had announced that Great Aunty Jill was coming, Oscar had shouted, "Hooray!" But he hadn't waited to finish his mouthful of peas before he spoke.

The peas had flown across the room and landed on the cat, who woke with a start and jumped onto the table in fright. It knocked over the salt and pepper and sent the dinner plates crashing to the floor.

What a mess!
"I'm sorry!" said Oscar.
But it had been too late.

Oscar thought he would try to cheer himself up. So he went downstairs to play at the dining room table. But he was still feeling sad when his mother found him sitting there.

"It's no good, Oscar," she said. "I know how much you like Great Aunty Jill, but after the mess you made at the table yesterday you can't eat with us tonight."

After his mother had gone to the kitchen to tidy up, Oscar burst into tears and put his head on the table.

"It's not fair," said Oscar to himself, "I don't *mean* to misbehave." He looked at the old table that had been his great grandmother's. "If only someone could help me," he said, and he started to cry again.

"I can," whispered a voice.
Oscar stopped crying and looked round. There wasn't anybody there.

"I can help you," said the voice again.

'Who was it? What was it?' thought Oscar.

"I'm down here!" said the voice.

Oscar's eyes opened wide as he realised that it was the table speaking to him.

"Don't be frightened," said the table, "I can help you."

"You can?" Oscar stammered. "You really will?"

"Yes," said the table. "I am so old, in fact I'm antique. Lots of boys and girls have sat around me, so I've learned a great deal about table manners."

Oscar stared in amazement. "You really can help me? What should I do?" His tears started to disappear, but how silly – he was talking to a table!

"Now listen carefully," said the table. "First, we must persuade your mother to let you stay up. Then you must really behave well at the table. I can certainly help you with the second part. It's the first problem that worries me."

"It worries me too," said Oscar. "Mummy never changes her mind and I know she will not let me stay up tonight."

"Nothing is impossible," said the table. "It just needs some thought."

At that moment Oscar's mother came back into the room. "What are you still doing in here? Did I hear you talking to yourself?"

"I'm thinking," said Oscar with a smile. "Is there anything I may do to help you, as Great Aunty Jill is coming?" he said.

"Oh, how nice of you, Oscar," said
his mother. "I would love some help."

"Perhaps I will go and tidy my bedroom first, then come and see if there is anything else I can do?"

Oscar's mother looked at him suspiciously. "Thank you, Oscar. That is really very kind of you."

'Why is he being so helpful?' she thought.

It was nearly 4 o'clock and Great Aunty Jill would be arriving soon.

"Oscar, Oscar," called his mother.

"I'm here, Mummy," he called, as he ran into the kitchen.

"I've been thinking," said his mother. "You have been so helpful this afternoon that I am going to let you stay up for our meal with Great Aunty Jill."

Oscar tried not to smile.

"On one condition," said his mother. "If you misbehave you will have to finish your meal on your own."

Oscar looked solemn. "Yes, Mummy, I understand," he said.

Oscar was so excited he couldn't wait to go and talk to the table.

Oscar rushed back to the table. Had he been
dreaming, or had the table really spoken to him?
He sat on a chair and looked at the table. "I've done
my part, now it's up to you to help me tonight."
To Oscar's delight and surprise the table chuckled.

"That isn't a problem," it said. "You have nothing to worry about. Just trust me."

Oscar wasn't so sure – anything could happen.

Later that evening, Oscar took his place at the table next to Great Aunty Jill. His father sat at the top of the table, his mother at the other end and his sister, Sarah, opposite Great Aunty Jill.

Oscar's mother looked very worried.

His father looked quite anxious.

They were wondering what Oscar might get up to,
especially as they knew the pudding was a very wobbly trifle.

Sarah looked very pleased with herself. She felt sure that her brother would get into trouble. And if he did, she wouldn't be able to stop herself giggling, even though she'd be in trouble then too.

"It's nice that you have both joined us tonight," said Aunty Jill, looking at the two children. "That makes it a special occasion."

"It *is* special," said Oscar, leaning across the table. "Would you like some bread?"

He picked up the plate of bread rolls, but unfortunately he did not look at what he was doing, and they spilled onto her lap.

"Thank you, Oscar," said Great Aunty Jill with a smile. "I only need one."

Oscar's mother and father looked at one another as Oscar hurriedly put the bread rolls back on the plate.

"Don't do that again," whispered the table. "Try not to touch anything. Just sit and smile and make polite conversation. It's all right, Oscar, you are doing fine. Trust me."

"Sorry, Aunty," said Oscar, as he put his elbows on the table in despair.

"No elbows on the table either," came a whisper.

The meal went very well. The table whispered and nudged Oscar to remind him not to hold his knife and fork in the air when eating, not to talk with his mouth full and not to play with his food.

In fact, with the help of Oscar's new friend, his table manners were excellent. His parents could hardly believe it, but they were also rather worried, as they thought he was talking to himself.

"Who are you talking to, Oscar?" asked his mother.

"Just a friend," said Oscar.

"Really? But there is nobody else here," replied his mother.

"I'm sure he's got a friend," said Great Aunty Jill. "I had one when I was Oscar's age, especially when I was eating at the table." She looked at Oscar and winked.

'Oh, no,' thought Oscar. 'Has she guessed? What will she say next?'

"When I was young my manners were terrible," continued Great Aunty Jill, "and I just had to learn how to behave, but I did get some help. If I told you where from, you would never believe me."

Then Great Aunty Jill started talking about something else. Oscar gave her a puzzled look. Did she know?

His mother then placed the bowl of wobbly trifle in the middle of the table.

Oscar was so pleased he was doing so well that he thought he would help Great Aunty Jill to some trifle. He picked up a spoon.

"Would you like some trifle, Great Aunty Jill?" he asked.

Oscar's mother stood up, Oscar's father looked the other way and Sarah put her hands over her eyes. The cat shot under the table.

I wonder what
happened next...